Wallace –

Happy Christmas

from your faithful companion

Gromit

Published by Ladybird Books Ltd
A Penguin Company
Penguin Books Ltd, 80 Strand, London, WC2R 0RL, England
Penguin Books Australia Ltd, Camberwell, Victoria, Australia
Penguin Group (NZ), cnr Airborne and Rosedale Roads, Albany,
Auckland 1310, New Zealand
All rights reserved

10 9 8 7 6 5 4 3 2 1

Ladybird and the device of a ladybird are trademarks
of Ladybird Books Ltd.

Manufactured in Italy

Personal information

Name: Wallace

Address: 62 West Wallaby St

Telephone: 2143

Height: 5'5"   Weight: satisfactory

Age: well   Allergies: gherkins bring me out in a rash

Notes: I do like a bit of cheese!!

Year Planner

JANUARY
M	T	W	T	F	S	S
					1	2
3	4	5	6	7	8	9
10	11	12	13	14	15	16
17	18	19	20	21	22	23
24	25	26	27	28	29	30
31						

FEBRUARY
M	T	W	T	F	S	S
	1	2	3	4	5	6
7	8	9	10	11	12	13
14	15	16	17	18	19	20
21	22	23	24	25	26	27
28						

MARCH
M	T	W	T	F	S	S
	1	2	3	4	5	6
7	8	9	10	11	12	13
14	15	16	17	18	19	20
21	22	23	24	25	26	27
28	29	30	31			

APRIL
M	T	W	T	F	S	S
				3	4	5
4	5	6	7	10	11	12
11	12	13	14	17	18	19
18	19	20	21	24	25	26
25	26	27	28			

JULY
M	T	W	T	F	S	S
				2	3	4
4	5	6	7	9	10	11
11	12	13	14	16	17	18
18	19	20	21	23	24	25
25	26	27	28	30		

OCTOBER
M	T	W	T	F	S	S
				1	2	3
3	4	5	6	8	9	10
10	11	12	13	15	16	17
17	18	19	20	22	23	24
24	25	26	27	29	30	31
31						

Useful information

Length
12 inches = 1 foot
3 feet = 1 yard
5½ yards = 1 rod, pole or perch
40 poles = 1 furlong
8 furlongs = 1 mile
3 miles = 1 league

Nautical Measure
6 feet = 1 fathom
608 feet = 1 cable
6080 feet = 1 nautical mile

Surveying Measure
7.92 inches = 1 link
100 links = 1 chain
80 chains = 1 mile

Cloth & Ribbon Measure
2¼ inches = 1 nail
4 nails = 1 quarter
4 quarters = 1 yard
5 quarters = 1 ell
6 quarters = 1 French ell

Cotton, Yarn and Silk Measure
1½ yards = 1 thread
120 yards = 1 skein
7 skeins = 1 hank
18 hanks = 1 spindle

Area
144 square inches = 1 square foot
9 square feet = 1 square yard
30¼ square yards = 1 square pole, rod or perch
16 square poles = 1 square chain
40 square poles = 1 rood
4 roods = 1 acre
10 square chains = 1 acre
640 acres = 1 square mile

Weight
16 drams = 1 ounce
16 ounces = 1 pound
14 pounds = 1 stone
28 pounds = 1 quarter
4 quarters = 1 hundredweight
20 hundredweight = 1 ton

Volume
5 fluid ounces = 1 gill
4 gills = 1 pint
2 pints = 1 quart
4 quarts = 1 gallon
2 gallons = 1 peck
8 gallons = 1 bushel
8 bushels = 1 quarter
36 bushels = 1 chaldron

Liquid Measure
2 pints = 1 quart
4 quarts = 1 gallon
9 gallons = 1 firkin
2 firkins = 1 kilderkin
2 kilderkins = 1 barrel
3 kilderkins = 1 hogshead
2 hogsheads = 1 butt

Notable British Dates

New Year's Day: January 1

Epiphany : January 6

Burn's Night: January 25

Accession of Queen Elizabeth II: February 6

St. Valentine's Day: February 14

St. David's Day: March 1

Commonwealth Day: March 8

St. Patrick's Day: March 17

Shrove Tuesday (Mardi Gras): the day before Ash Wednesday

Ash Wednesday, the first day of Lent: forty days before Easter

Easter Sunday: the first Sunday after the first full moon on or after March 21

British Summertime begins: the first Sunday after March 21

Queen Elizabeth II Birthday: April 21

St. George's Day: April 23

Ascension Day: forty days after Easter

Whit-Sunday: seven weeks after Easter

Trinity Sunday: eight weeks after Easter

British Summertime ends: usually the last Sunday in October

Halloween: October 31

Bonfire Night: November 5

Remembrance Sunday: the first Sunday after November 11

St. Andrew's Day: November 30

Advent Sunday: fourth Sunday before Christmas Day

Christmas Eve: December 24

Christmas Day: December 25

Boxing Day (St. Stephen's Day): December 26

New Year's Eve/Hogmanay: December 31

Notable British Cheeses

Buxton Blue
Caerphilly
Cheddar
Cheshire
Cornish Yarg
Derby
Double Gloucester
Dovedale

Grafton Village Cheddar
Lancashire
Lincolnshire Poacher
Red Leicester
Sage Derby
Shropshire Blue
Somerset Brie
Stilton

Stinky Bishop
Ticklemore
Wensleydale

Cheese Types: Blue, Cheddars, Creamy, Goat, Sharp, Sheep, Smoked, and Stinky

Week 1   RESOLUTIONS

Monday

Stay on top of paperwork (file all scraps in journal)
Keep cellar tidy (to please Gromit)
Watch my weight (tank tops are a bit of a squeeze)

Anything for you, Gromit?   Try harder with greenhouse

Tuesday

✳ ✳ ✳ ✳ ✳

Bumped into Mrs Mulch at Harvey's Vegetables just now.

She's having a spot of bother with rabbits in her garden, virtually decimating her pumpkins she says.

Then it came to me . . . Gromit and I should form some kind of 'humane pest control' setup. (There's no need to harm the little bunnies now.)

cracking idea!

Gromit'll love it!

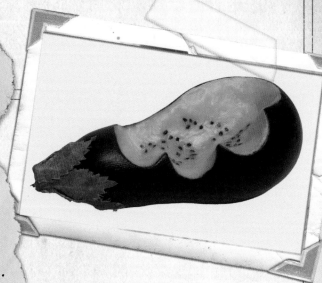

Write Christmas thank you letters.
Return Gromit's knitted dog coat.

Secret stashes of cheese:

* Bookshelf (Grated Expectations, East of Edam, Brie Encounter)

Sunday

* Socks (cheesy-smelling ones)
* Videos (Fromage to Eternity)
* Toothpaste tube

Monday

Wallace: Clean cellar please!   G.

Renew subscription to 'Ay-up' magazine

10am inaugural Veg Growers' Committee Meeting.
Agenda 1. Chairman nomination
2. The Vegetable Show

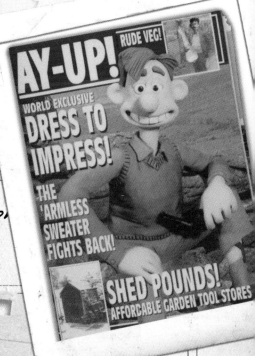

AY-UP! RUDE VEG!

WORLD EXCLUSIVE
DRESS TO IMPRESS!

THE 'ARMLESS SWEATER FIGHTS BACK!

SHED POUNDS!
AFFORDABLE GARDEN TOOL STORES

TO DO
- Think of a name.
  Bunnies R Us....
  The Verminators....
  The Pest People....
  Pesto . . .
  Anti-pesto....hmmmm
- compile list of potential clients
  (Mrs Mulch for one)
- Work out essential equipment needed for business (natty uniforms a must)
- Try again to convince Gromit that it's a good idea

Friday

Sunday

More cheese stashes:
* cassette Tapes (All Things Brie and Wonderful)
* Telephone

Week 3

Monday

Order uniforms

Tuesday

Wednesday

Veg Grov
Commi

Thursday

Friday

Sa

Veg Growers Committee Meeting Minutes

New Chairman

Nominees for chairman:
1 Mr Crock   2 Mr Growbag
Votes for Mr Crock   1 (himself)
Votes for Mr Growbag 25
Mr Growbag duly nominated as chairman by 25-1.
Mr Growbag proceeded to give a rousing acceptance speech. Mr Crock's heckles of You'll all rot in hell led to his eventual exclusion from the church hall.

The Vegetable Show

Date set for 17 September, venue Tottington Hall. Only 33 weeks to go!!!!!
It was concluded that a letter be drawn up conveying the committee's appreciation of Lady Tottington's continuing hospitality and support for the event.
Wallace has volunteered to present her Ladyship with said letter in person, should it be required.

Week 4

Monday - book Gromit's 'To a Dear Dog - Happy Birthday' greeting in The Morning Post.

Present ideas
1 - Gardening book - "Potting with Paws"
2 - electric blanket for marrow
3 - alarm for greenhouse door
4 - Subscription to "The Germinator"
5 - Jumbo bot. Veg-B-Big

POSTED

ORDERED

Gromit's birthday!

Week 5

Monday

Tuesday

Library - g
'Gardening
for Dogs'

Gromit has finally come round to my cracking business idea (I think the rabbit droppings he found in the greenhouse helped).

So, it's all systems go!! We've got the name 'Anti-pesto - Humane Pest Control' (pretty nifty, eh?) and have found the perfect van for the job. An Austin A35, ideal for what we need, with plenty of room in the back.

cellar looks
a bit messy

✱ Must try out Wallace's new invention, 'The Electric Toilet Brush'.

Friday

** Wool Shop - eight balls - purple, cream, baby blue.

Now that we're going up in the world, Gromit's knitting me a new tank top!

Saturday

Put up Anti-pesto cards -
Greengrocers
Library   Wool shop
Post Office
Allotments
Church noticeboard

Sunday

Monday

* Wallace's electric toilet brush a little too vigorous — bathroom (and me) soaked. Suggest Wallace adds variab[le] speed controls.

Clean out cellar (make room for rabbits??)

Investigate rabbit storage methods — how big do hutches come? How high can you stack them?

WHILE YOU WERE OUT

To   Wallace

From

Tel. No.

Please call back	X
Will call again	
Urgent	

MESSAGE

Cheese shop left note — your delivery is too big for van, need to arrange alternative

Taken by

Date

Shopping List

Carrots (4 boxes[)]
Vegetables (for Wallace)
Bones (for me)
Bathroom cleaner

CHEDDAR

Please Gromit?

A Snip!!

RECEIVED

HOP 2 IT

Week 7

Monday

Pick up Anti-pesto overalls,
caps and boots

Overalls smashing - very snug.
Must call to pass on my
compliments

Receipt pad?

Petty cash slips?

Thursday

Need suitable
rabbit catcher
implements
(grabbers and nets)
along with some

Friday

almost-new
potato sacks

Saturday

Return library books: Th
Great Dane Escape and
Gardening for Dogs

Pretty
natty,
eh?

Monday

Pick up new newspaper [RECEIVED]
advertisement and Anti-
pesto stationery.

esday

...lay

Stamps, stickers and
cards all sorted —
we're ready for
business!

    I have a bad
    feeling about
    this.

                    G.

Week 9

Monday

Tuesday

We have lift-off! Miss Thripp called on the Anti-pesto 'hot-line' to say she was in desperate need of our services. 'Always happy to be of assistance', Gromit and I jumped into the van and - Geronimo! - we were off to our first appointment! On arrival, we caught two of the trespassing rabbits, and installed and activated Anti-pesto security devices. Subjects disarmed and neutralised. Job well done, I'd say!

Wednesday

Thursday

Friday

Saturday

Clean cellar.

Week 10

* Tuesday 10 am - return to Miss Thripps. Squirrels have now been seen scaling fence and abseiling down the Anti-pesto emergency cord, thus setting off intruder alarms at HQ - two false alarms over the weekend. We need to work out some way to stop them sharpish.

* Veg Grower's committee Meeting

Tuesday

ednesday

Thursday

Thursday 12 am - Miss Thripp's anti-squirrel devices installed and activated.

Friday

Friday 9am - two more calls from clients! Mr Windfall and Mrs Mulch !!

Saturd

Need more hutches and a bigger ladder.

Week 11

Monday

Mr Windfall 9.30 am.
    Reviewed security & set alarms –
no pests (yet). As Mr Windfall is allergic to
rabbits, he'd rather be safe than sorry.

Tuesday

Wednesd

Thursday

Friday

Saturday

Veg Growers Committee Meeting Minutes

The Vegetable Show
The Vicar requested that competitors
for this years Vegetable Show maintain
a little more neighbourliness than
exhibited over previous years. Certain
unwarranted actions have already come
to his notice, with sightings of
binocular-clad competitors spying on
fellow vegetable growers and, as yet
unconfirmed, rummaging of compost
bins. Aggressive tendencies of this
kind will not be tolerated.

With some regret, last years winner
returned the Golden Carrot to Lady
Tottington for
safe-keeping.

Invoice to:
Miss Thripp

I have the pleasure of enclosing
an invoice for payment covering:

Capture and removal of pests
Installation of Anti-pesto
security devices
'Rapid Response' call-out fee
                Total: Ten Pounds

Payment terms – as soon as
possible please. Cash preferred;
goods in kind (such as live
poultry or vegetables) are not
acceptable.

We trust that you found our
services of the highest merit,
and assure you that we are always
happy to be of assistance.

Wallace & Gromit
(Anti-pesto S.W.A.T Team)

FILE COPY

Monday

POSTED

Tuesday

Library – Tess of
the D'Obermans

Wednesday

Thursday

We make a cracking team!

Friday

Sunday

Week 13

Made decision for show – large marrow, Tiger Cross variety.

Monday

Van needs following items installed:

Interior back
1. 'Quarantine constriction unit' (rabbit cage)
2. Carrot odour emitter and tape player (to calm upset bunnies)

Interior front
1. Bunny detectors
2. Mug holders

Also ask garage about de-mudding device?

PACKED O[...]

Tuesday

Wednesday

Seen my dibber anywhere?  L O S T

April Fools' Day. Try out my 'noiseless whoopee cushion' invention on Gromit. It's 'silent but deadly'!

Sunday

Discovered cheese in Wallace's socks and on bookshelf. Buy mousetraps and start Wallace on weight-loss programme.

Monday

Check Miss Thripp got invoice - no reply yet

Cushion not a great success. Might need a rethink.

esday

Have just put the finishing touches to our new rabbit vacuum system. Decided we needed a clever rabbit-catching device for large-scale operations, a system that sucks the little rascals out of their burrows and into the hands of yours truly. Ingenious!

SUBJECT DISARMED AND NEUTRALISED

ursday

Think I've also cracked our 'rapid response' technique. We need to be on the road in a matter of seconds, so need some kind of nifty 'launch system'. Perhaps I'll have a think over a nice slice of Wensleydale....

Friday

ALARM

WAKE-UP → OVERALLS

TEA!! ←

→ VAN STARTED

→ ANTI-PESTO ARE GO!

Sunday

STED

Week 15

Monday

CALL MISS THRIPP

Tuesd

Wedne

Thursda

Friday

Saturday

Veg Growers Committee Meeting Minutes

Slugs

Chairman Mr Growbag gave a most illuminating talk on slugs (a subject close to his heart following the devastations of the Slug Blight in '32). The best method involves planting cups of beer near to affected areas - slugs will be drawn to the smell, fall into the cups and end their days in a drunken stupor. It was agreed that this method was preferable to those undertaken by Mr Crock (i.e. catapulting the poor creatures at neighbours or posting them to perceived vegetable show competitors). Several volunteers offered to supply leftover beer to association members.

Biscuits

Meeting also concluded (by a majority of 27-2) that chocolate hob-nobs were preferable to fig rolls. Mrs Girdling kindly offered to organise for next meeting.

Bit worried about cash flow - how about getting a lodger in? Discuss with Gromit.

SORTED

No - not after the last time.

Monday

May we remind you of our invoice
dated 21 March.

Payment covers:
Capture and removal of pests
Installation of Anti-pesto
security devices (to include a
SECOND visit to install anti-
squirrel devices)
Rapid response call out fee.

Payment is required within 10
days (cash only).

POSTED

Always happy to be of assistance
Wallace & Gromit
(Anti-pesto S.W.A.T. Team)

9pm – Citizen
Kanine (favourite
film) on TV.

Tuesday

re you ever
going to clean
he cellar?

Wednesday

Definitely
Gromit, as soon
as I get a minute

Thursday

'Quarantine constriction
unit', carrot odour
emitter, tape player (set
up to play 'Run Rabbit
Run') and mug holders
installed.
Further discussion needed
re. bunny detectors and
de-mudding device.

REPLIED

Need:
Box of carrots
Lettuces
Celery
Disinfectant
String
Crackers

Week 17

Monday

Strange things are going on! I was picking up some elastic bands in town, when I caught Miss Thripp darting down the back alley beside Harvey's Veg. She even left her trolley behind!

Tuesday

Had a crackin' idea for our launch system - a map of the town to pinpoint alarms when they go off. Shouldn't be too tricky, I've still got plenty of twin-core-and-earth.

SORTED

WHILE YOU WERE OUT

To _____ Wallace

From _____

Tel. No. _____

Please call back	
Will call again	
Urgent	

MESSAGE

Printers called - leaflets ready

G.

Taken by _____

Date _____

Time _____

PICKED UP

Saturday

Sunday

Need:
3 boxes of carrots
Extra-strong disinfectant
48 lightbulbs

Week 18

Monday

Tuesday

Wednesday

One more satisfied customer!
Our mission: Mrs Mulch
and her GIANT PUMPKIN
(it's a beauty). Launch
systems were activated
(it worked a treat)
and Anti-pesto saved
the day! Mrs M said it
was bad but it was pure
vegetable carnage when we
got there!

SUBJECT DISARMED AND NEUTRALISED

DELIVERED

Your turn to empty
hutches - gone to
library

Can you take back that
'Clockwork Orange' book
(not at all what I
expected, very little
automated fruit)

Saturday

Greenhouse cleared,
soil prepared. Need
more manure - ask
Wallace*

*to order some

Creatures at your carrots
Beasties got your brassicas
Monsters munching your marrows

WE CAN HELP!
Fast - Neat - Efficient
NO ANIMALS HARMED IN PROCESS

ANTI-PESTO
S.W.A.T. TEAM

Call Anti-Pesto Today!

Week 19

Monday

Tuesday

Wednesday

Thursday

Friday

Veg Growers Committee Meeting Minutes

17 WEEKS TO GO UNTIL THE COMPETITION!!
Lady Tottington presented the meeting with
her plans for the Vegetable Competition.
Points 1 and 2 on the agenda were:

Advertising and Promotion
The promotions agency for Veg-B-Big have
written to Lady Tottington enquiring
whether they can be of service in
promoting the event. Sample posters and
banners will be provided in due course and
the committee will decide on this at a
future date.

Entertainment and Stalls
As is usual, refreshments will be provided
by the local WI, and the Wallaby St
Brownies will run the tombola. Lady
Tottington has written to the Old Trout
pub informing them of the committees
decision not to put on a Beer Tent this
year (following last year's incident
                with Mr Crock).

Need:
More dog shampoo (I smell
of rabbit)
5 boxes carrots
a bigger shovel

More Wensleydale -
we've run out (again)

Sunday

Launch System managed
to put three sugars in
my tea today - check
calibration

SORTED OUT

Petty Cash

No:

Date:

Amount

or what required:

For printing
500 leaflets

37 pounds

PAID

Signature: Gromit

Approved:

Invoice to: Mrs Mulch

I have the pleasure of
enclosing an invoice for
payment covering:

Capture of pests and
installation of Anti-pesto
security devices
Rapid response call out fee
                    Total: 9 pounds

We trust that you found our
services of the highest
merit, and assure you that
we are always happy to be
of assistance.
Wallace & Gromit
(Anti-pesto S.W.A.T Team)

Library — The
Scarlet Lettuce

Spotted Lady
Tottington through
my binoculars today.
She looked grand.

Friday

Sunday

Beds prepared and filled
ready for planting!

Week 21

Mon

Tue

W

Tested Wallace's new 'pocket lawnmower' invention today.

Thanks Gromit

Plus points:
Perfect cutting action
Smooth, easy handling
Easy to carry

Minus points:
Needs refuelling every two minutes
Not really suitable for lawns any bigger than a few centimetres.

Bonsai?

VERDICT: back to the drawing board.

Thursday

A great idea – we need a client gallery, with portraits of all our regulars. Could light up when they call us – will look into.

Friday

Your turn to feed rabbits, I'm off to the cinema – 'The Man With The Golden Delicious'

Saturday

Sun

To Do:

Call Mr Browning about his organic carrots – apparently bunnies can't resist them!

To Miss Thripp
I refer to our recent correspondence
and several messages left on your
phone, with neighbours, etc.
regarding payment of our bill. Please
can you give this matter your
immediate attention or devices will
need to be removed.
Yours regretfully,
Wallace & Gromit
(Anti-pesto S.W.A.T. Team)

DELIVERED

Seedlings are coming out,
thin soon

HILE YOU WERE OUT

Wallace

Please call back	
Will call again	
Urgent	

MESSAGE

Miss Thripp called —
cheque is in post!

Taken by   Gromit
Date
Time

Bumped into Lady
Tottington in town.
Suddenly came over
all hot and bothered
wonder if I'm falling
for something?

Sunday

Monday

Tuesday

**MISS THRIPP
CHEQUE
BOUNCED!!!**

Wednesday

NO ANSWER

Thursday

Veg Growers Committee Meeting Minutes

VEGETABLE COMPETITION
Advertising and Promotion
Secretary to write to Veg-B-Big to thank them for their 'Get a Load of These Big Ones' posters but their services will not be required this year. It was resolved that the advertising will take a more restrained approach, with the usual Vegetable Competition banners and posters, newspaper editorials etc.

Entertainment and Stalls
Gay Bunting Industries have been booked and Mr Caliche has kindly offered to man a gardening supplies stall. Amusements for younger visitors include the Battle of Britain helter-skelter ride and the Tottington Hall bouncy castle (deemed safe this year due to the absence of the Beer Tent although the under-14s-only rule needs to be strictly enforced.)

Our Valued Clients

Library – 'Animal Farm'
no use at all

...unday
Seedlings thinned, slug
defences set up.

Week 24

Don't know what to do about Mrs Thripp. She seemed really sorry about the cheque but I can't help feeling that she just isn't going to pay up.

Not many people remember her conviction of fraud after the Giant Vegetable Competition of '72 (the tomato is a fruit, not a vegetable...). Perhaps if I remind her of this, it might just speed things up...

SUBJECT DISARMED AND NEUTRALISED

Monday

Gromit - can anything be done about the smell of rabbits?

Tuesday

No.

WHILE YOU WERE OUT

To **Wallace**

From _____

Tel. No. _____

Please call back	
Will call again	
Urgent	

MESSAGE

Library called - can you return 'East of Edam', now overdue

Taken by _____ RETURNED

Date _____

Time _____

Need:

8 boxes of carrots
Deodorant for hutches
Van wax
Low-cal crackers
Rabbit food (for W)

Sunday

I was hoping for a nice slice of Gorgonzola but we seem to have run out. (And if I come across another mousetrap again....)

Monday

Tuesday

Wednes

Thursday

Launch activation needs checking – it keeps dropping me a bit heavily into the van. As if I weighed more than I actually do.

Frida

Plants coming on nicely. Custom feeding regime seems to be working.

Saturday

Need:

12 boxes of carrots

Industrial-strength deodorant

Veg-B-Big fleece/blanket for marrows

Size 5 needles & 6 balls of merino – colour?

can't we get a little more cheese? Just a couple of pounds?

No.

Monday

Tuesday

nesday

hursday

Friday

Sunday

Anti-pesto is working a treat! Our first payment is in the bank (finally) AND we've clocked up a number of satisfied customers.

And the 'Bun-Vac 6000' is proving most effective. The cellar is full to the brim with our vegetable-munching friends. And they love their carrots — Gromit really has his work cut out for him.

...ar needs ...eaning

Hope we've got enough hutches.

...ore wool ...needed

Launch system all seems fine. Not sure what's wrong.

Week 27

Monday
Where's Gromit? He's in the greenhouse again!

Tuesday

Wednesday

Pests to guard against:
- Mice
- Red Spider Mites
- Aphids
- Greenhouse whitefly
- Millipedes
- Woodlice
- Greenfly
- Flea beetles
- Slugs
- Snails
- Rabbits?
- Squirrels
- Caterpillars

Thursday

Fancy a night at the cinema, Gromit? They're showing 'Carrot on a Hot Tin Roof'.

Friday

Discovered that Mrs Mulch always adds underpants to her compost. Perhaps I should give that a go with a pair of Wallace's?

Saturday

Week 28

catch up with invoices! Monday

...ke cash and
...eques to bank

...ash and Tuesday
...polish van

...ED OUT

Wednesday

Problems in the Marrow

Look out for:
Mosaic virus
Eelworm
Root rot
Botrytis
Gummosis
Anthracnose (leaf spot)
Sclerotina
Black Rot
Blotch
Stem Rot
Verticillium Wilt
Mildew
Sun Scald

...o:
...all

...he pleasure of
...g an invoice for
...covering:

Return 'Brie
Encounter' to library.
Pick up 'The Plant
Suite' LP for Gromit

Capture of pests
utilising nets
Cabbages secured and
security systems installed
        Total: 13 pounds

Marrow polish? Saturday

I think Gromit is
knitting a tanktop
for his marrow –
maybe he's taking this
too far?

Wallace & Gromit
(Anti-pesto S.W.A.T Team)
Always happy to be of
assistance

Week 29

Monday —

Tuesday

This diet Gromit's had me on is no fun. I just can't resist a nice bit of cheese. What's needed is a bit of 'technological innovation' – some kind of 'mind-manipulation' contraption that provides all the willpower you need.

Think I'll take myself down to the cellar and have a tinker. Now, where's that Gorgonzola? It's good for the old mental stimulation you know.

Need:
Heavy-duty wiring grid
Brain-wave
monitor/amplifier
Neural transmitter
module
Comfy chair

Petty Cash

For what required:

100 keyrings for

Anti-pesto

Cash on delivery

gnature: Approv

Saturday
Gone to cinema to
see 'A Sweetcorn
Named Desire'. Y
turn to feed rabbits

Monday

Getting quite used to these vegetables now — and I do like to nibble a carrot from time to time.

Does rabbit poo make good manure?

Date .... No. ....
Received
from   Mr Windfall ....
The sum of £15 ....
For supply of Anti-Pesto services as
                            necessary

Cash
Cheque
Discount   ....

WITH THANKS

Wednesday

Have put Lady Tottington in pride of place over the fire, in a beautiful frame.

Thursday

Gromit — is this of any interest to you?

Friday

Mr Growbag's History of The Great Vegetable Show

The Great Vegetable Competition dates back to the 450s when it was established by the then occupant of Tottington Hall, Montague Cantaloupe of Orange. Since then, it has battled with a multitude of major setbacks, including The Great Mole Incursion of 1527, The Poodle Panic of 1792, The Great Table Collapse of 1841, The Compost Scandal of '22, not to mention The Spade and Hoe Shortage of 1941-45. I intend to cover each of these events in exhaustive detail, as well as introducing

Need:
18 boxes of carrots
Celery for Wallace
Lots more sacks
Noseplugs
More dog shampoo
Bot. veg-B-Big
Soft cloths for
polishing marrow

Monday

Tuesday

SORTED

Veg Growers Committee Meeting Minutes

Behaviour
P.C. Mackintosh has made another special plea for orderliness amongst competitors this year. Tension has again reached endemic proportions and he has already noted some illegal acts amongst those present. Upturned rakes, sharpened trowels, rat poison, not to mention the unfriendliness about Mrs Girdling (as seen on the show poster at Harveys Vegetables), have NOT escaped his attention.

Entertainment and stalls
By popular demand, a Bag-a-bunny shooting gallery and Whack-a-bunny stall have been booked for the show. As a replacement for the beer tent, Wallace has put in a special request for a cheese tent - tbc.

Saturday

Tried Mind-o-Matic for the first time. Singed my ears — needs more tinkering.

Van needs cleaning Gromit   Too busy

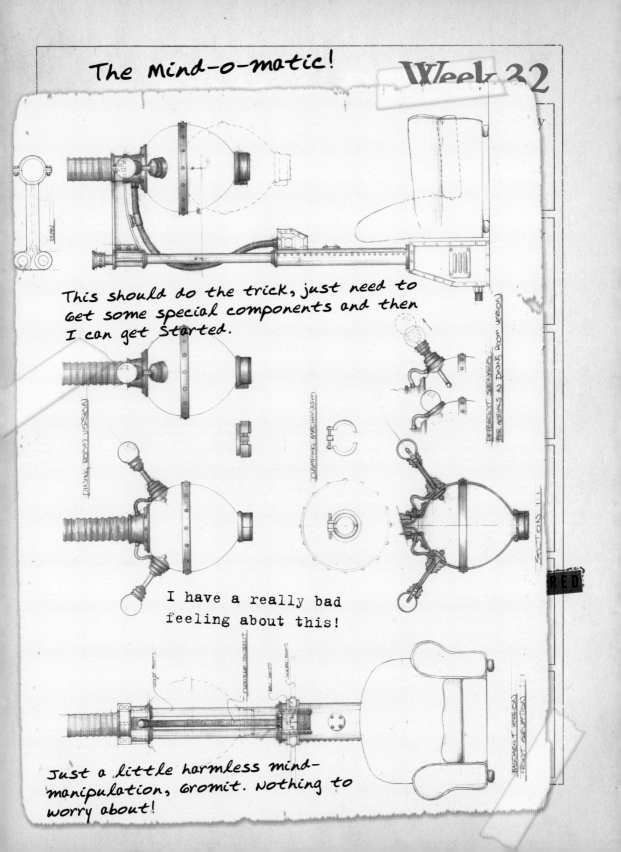

Week 33

Monday Maintenance checks on all Anti-pesto alarms around town - to̶d̶ ̶a̶n̶d̶ ̶ ̶t̶o̶morrow

Only four weeks to go until the big day and it feels like the competition's hotting up. It's been 'action stations' at Anti-pesto.

Tottington Hall have released to the media some rather nice pre-Vegetable competition photographs of Lady Campanula Tottington. Have ordered in another large version just to show my support.

Thursday

Send out invoices &

Friday

Take cash to bank

Saturday

Oil, water, wax and polish van - got to give the right impression!

Good Luck Boys X

To _____
From __Anti-pesto__
Tel. No. _____

| Please call back |
| Will call again |
| Urgent |

MESSAGE

Mrs Girdling called

Mr Dibber ditto

Mr Caliche ditto

Gromit, did you wash
my overalls a bit hot?
They seem to have
shrunk a bit.
Nothing to do with me.

Monday

Tuesday

Wednesday

Thursday

Special pre-Vegetable Competition Church Service

Hymn *(all stand)*: 'Come Thou Almighty King Edward'

Prayer led by the Vicar:

'Our Father who art in heaven, marrow be thy name, thy will be done, thy digging done in the earth as it is in heaven. Oh give us this day our daily veg and forgive us our trellis. Lead us not into temptation but deliver us our vegetation low carb dietary supplements. For thine is the garden, the allotment and the greenhouse for ever and ever. Amen.'

Hymn *(all stand)*: 'Cucumber My Lord'

Need:
24 boxes of carrots
More hutches?
Disinfectant
Penetrating oil
Gloves for lifting
marrow

Gromit, can you get
me some more razors
(seem to be a bit
hairier these days)?

Monday

Tuesday

Wednesday

Thursday

<u>Veg Growers Committee Meeting Minutes</u>

It was agreed to keep the meeting as short as possible, as members were eager to get back to their plants. After the third round of tea and biscuits, some members began boasting and arguing over the relative merits of their produce. The meeting was eventually broken up after 3 hours on the instructions of P. C. Mackintosh.

PACKED OFF

Gave out some more stickers and leaflets!

PROTECTED BY ANTI PESTO

PROTECTED BY ANTI PESTO

WHILE YO

To _Anti-pest_

From

Tel. No.

Please call

Will call again

Urgent

MESSAGE

Mr Mulch, Mr Growbag and Mr Crock called – check alarms

SORTED OUT

Taken by

Date

Time

RED UP

Sunday Water marrows and check greenhouse security locks

Caught Gromit vacuuming his marrows... should I be worried?

SUBJECT DISARMED AND N

Week 36

...onday

...sday

...ay

...day

Give the
Bun-Vac a
once-over.

FIXE

This diet Gromit's had me on has really
put a spring in my step! I'm bounding up
those cellar steps like a bunny!
Extraordinary!
Wonder if the presence of all these
rabbits is somehow affecting me?

Book appointment at dentist - front
teeth could do with a nice polish.

RE OUT

...sto

MESSAGE

- Gromit to order in another
  10 crates of carrots
- Wash overalls (a bit whiffy)

Call Mr Windfall - his
cabbages are in dire need
of protection.

Monday 12th

Only 5 days to go until the giant
vegetable competition! Getting so busy
I've had to add in pages to our journal.

Initiate
'Operation Marrow!'

ILE YOU WERE OUT

Anti-pesto

WHILE YOU WERE OUT

To ___ Anti-pesto
From ___
Tel. No. ___

Please call back	
Will call again	
Urgent	

successful operation
at Mrs Mulch's
tonight (rabbits up
to their usual
mischief). Gromit
bagged the little
monster and he's now
tucked away in our
cellar. Job well done
eh lad!

THE MORNING POST
THE PAPER WITH IT'S FINGER ON THE PULSES

HUMANE PEST CONTROL TRIUMPHS AGAIN

RABBIT PROBLEM CONTAINED

Marrow escape for gardener

Tuesday 13th

Our first appointment with Lady Campanula Tottington!!! Think we're about to go up in the world....and I think we're going to like it!!

Tottington Hall has been rid of its rabbits! Lady Tottington appears to be a real fan of our humane handling techniques and the Bun-Vac did a cracking job (despite a spot of bother with a gentleman-friend of hers). Another client to add to the list, Gromit! And, I think we've left quite an impression with her Ladyship!

And inspiration truly struck tonight as I hit upon the solution to all our rabbit storage problems! Simply by connecting the Bun-Vac to the Mind-manipulation-o-matic we have successfully managed to brainwash one of the bunnies! Think we're on the cusp of a real breakthrough here – mankind rid of rabbits forever!

THE MORNING POST

NIGHT OF VEGETABLE CARNAGE!

ANTI-PESTO FAIL TO TURNIP IN TIME

Where was our crop protection?

Wednesday 14th

A beast has been on a vegetable-destroying rampage! The town is relying on us or Anti-pesto is ruined! We need some kind of bait... monster-size carrot? no...or HOW ABOUT A LOVELY LADY RABBIT! Yes, that's it! Now where's that Gromit got to...

10am - Church Hall, emergency committee meeting

Keep calm!

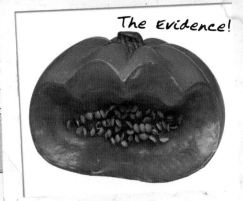

The Evidence!

WHILE YOU WERE OUT

To _Anti-pesto_

From _____

Tel. No. _____

Please call back	
Will call again	
Urgent	

MESSAGE

Miss Thripp called — wants her money back

Taken by _____

Date _____

...OUT

...back	
Will call again	
Urgent	

MESSAGE

PC Mackintosh called — he'd like to have a word

Thursday

All went wrong last night. Gromit went off on his own again, and I thought we were supposed to be a team! It's just not on!

BUT we've discovered who the beast is - it's Hutch!! The lunar panel of the Mind-o-matic must have over-stimulated Hutch's bunny nature!

The were-rabbit is...Wallace!! Must do something (check on marrow first).

Immediately dashed round to Tottington Hall to tell her Ladyship that we had captured the rabbit monster. She was most relieved, and even invited me up to her rooftop conservatory (or 'inner sanctum' as she calls it). We were having a lovely time until Gromit switched on the sprinkler system. Soaked we were - and ruined a perfectly good tank top, to say nothing of a relationship with an important client. I don't know what's got into that dog!

Mo

Tu

Friday 16th

Gromit thinks that I'm the beast!!! And just because my ears seem a little 'rabbit-like' these days. I told him it was just a reaction to the healthy veg diet he's had me on - it's the 'toxins' coming out.

Silly old pooch!

Take van into garage - fix door and remove giant paw prints. Can't let the public find out

Fri

One day until the Giant Vegetable Competition!! Stay vigilant.

Satur

Saturday

What a calamity! Turns out Gromit was right after all. I AM the beast. And there's NOTHING I can do about it! My mind's just a rabbity-mush and all I can remember from the vegetable show are lots of marauding gardeners, a man waving a gun at me and Gromit riding around on his marrow... not to mention waking up in the cheese tent without a scrap of clothes on and Lady Tottington by my side.

Marrow is ruined BUT Wallace is safe, and I don't think we'll be seeing the beast OR Victor Quartermaine again.

Week 43

Sunday 18th

Successfully reversed the mind manipulation process today and natural order has been restored. Hutch has been returned to rabbithood and I feel smashing. Although it's a bit of a blow to learn that Lady Tottington (Totty) is not a fan of my beloved cheese - or indeed anything dairy-like. And we were getting on so well...

The Golden Carrot Award is mine!!!

VICTORY!

THE MORNING POST

BEAST HOUNDED OUT OF TOWN

Monday 19th

11am Veg Growers Committee Meeting
postponed for two weeks (while competitors
recover).

The diet is officially off. It's no good
– you just can't change human nature –
it will only lead to problems. And I
don't know if I've mentioned this, but
I DO love a bit of Gorgonzola.

Big box of crackers
Gorgonzola
Cheddar
A nice bit of
Wensleydale...

Phone Harvey's Veg –
cancel carrots

Cinema – 'The Man Who
Grew Too Much'

Week 45

Monday

Tuesday

Veg Growers Committee Meeting Minutes

(Absentees - Wallace)

Our first meeting post-Great Vegetable Competition. Mr Growbag concluded that it was indeed an eventful day (of a similar scale to the Runaway Lawnmower of '48). It appears that the Were-rabbit problem has now been contained and gardeners can rest easy.

Congratulations were passed on to Gromit, recipient of this year's Golden Carrot Award in recognition of his marrow and tremendous bravery.

Mrs Mulch enquired as to whether anyone had seen her chainsaw, which she hasn't seen since the day of the Show.

Our Finest Hour!

Make more marrow chutney

Halloween. Must see if Mrs Mulch has any spare pumpkins.

Business has been quiet. The Anti-pesto 'hotline' has been silent since the competition. Still, it gives us a chance to put our feet up, eh Gromit?

And to finally clean the cellar!

WHILE YOU WERE OUT

To ——————————————

From ——————————————

Tel. No. ——————————————

Please call back	
Will call again	
Urgent	

MESSAGE

Phone engineer says there's nothing wrong with line.

Taken by ——————————————

Date ——————————————

Saturday

Bonfire Night. Keep Wallace away from fireworks this year.

Week 47

Monday

Wallace's
christmas
Pressie List:
Tank tops
Bigger cheese box
Socks
Ratchet
screwdriver

Tuesday

Wednesday

All I want is a
clean cellar...

Thursday

crikey!

Carol Service,
collection for
repairs to church

Christmas Eve -
drinks at Tottington
Hall. (Think I'll
stop in with a nice
slice of Stilton.)

Sunday

Christmas Day. I
think W deserves all
the trimmings

That was a cracking dinner yesterday Gromit! Well done lad!

Think this Anti-pesto lark is definitely a seasonal thing. Perhaps we need a new change of direction. Or how about another 'monster rabbit'! Ho Ho. Perhaps if I had just another look at the Mind-o-matic ....

Wednesday

Library - return 'Withering Sprouts'

Thursday

RESOLUTIONS

Stay on top of paperwork
Keep cellar tidy
Start work on my next invention, the everlasting cream cracker.

Friday

Only 36 weeks until the Vegetable Competition!!!

Sunday

HAPPY NEW YEAR!

Let's hope it's a quiet one...

Contacts

Mr and Mrs Mulch – tel 2768 (pumpkins)

Mr Growbag – tel 2986 – chairman (artichokes)

Vicar – tel 2666 (carrots and aubergines)

Mr Crock – tel 2114 (slug problem)

✳ Miss Thripp – tel 2076 ◁ NEEDS CHASING FOR PAYMENT

Mr Leaching – tel 2880

Lady Tottingdon (Totty) – tel 2001

Mr Windfall – tel 2143 (cabbages)

Mrs Girdling – tel 2576 (carrots and lettuces)

Mr Dibber – tel 2243 (potatoes)

Mr Caliche – tel 2456 – garden supplies

Victor ~~Quartermaine~~ – tel 2587

PC Mackintosh – tel 2901

(Police Station Vegetable Hotline – 2999)

Cheese Shop - tel 2118
(account number 001)
Garage - tel 2709
Wallaby Woollens - tel 215
Harvey's Vegetables - tel 2.
(carrot hotline - 2334)
Library - 2090
(Late returns and fines - 2
Wallaby Office Supplies - 2356
Pest Control Outfits Inc - 7012
Safe 'n' Sure Systems - 6700
Doctors - 2065
Vets - 2143
Rabbit Supplies (Wholesale) Ltd - 5578
Tank Tops-U-Like Mail Order - 9876
Acme Invention Supplies - 8012 **

Advertisements